Fergus Full Stop

is No●1

(Number One) Punc●

His job is to keep

the words and

sentences and other

Puncs in order●

Fergus is a traffic policeman.
Although he is round and fat,
he is very fit.

As well as being an all-round
sportsman, he is a member of
the P.D.D.T.
(Punc Daredevil Dsplay Team).

Fergus is very proud of his ancestors who, it is said, were the first Full Stops in history. They were the very first Puncs to sail across the seas and settle among different languages.

Wherever they went, they put things in order ● They were bold and strong, and turned words into sentences by bringing them to a ● They had big hands and powerful arms ● They knew how to stop trouble ●

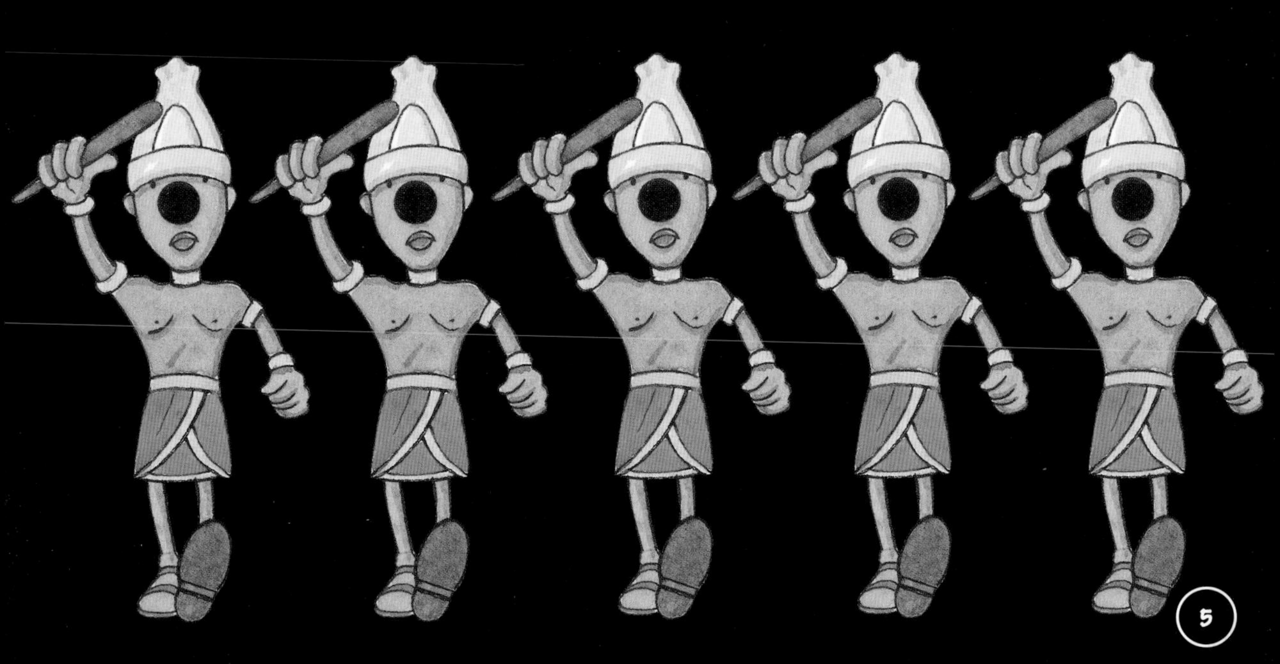

Even when he was only
a few months old,
Fergus looked as
though he would
grow up to
make things

STOP.

When he was given food he didn't like, such as spinach, semolina and lumpy custard, he would push the spoon away.

His mother knew that it was

time to STOP.

At school, his teachers found Fergus very helpful. If he saw boys fighting in the playground, he would rush in with his arms and fists swinging.

"STOP that,"

he would shout in his gruff voice. He was so strong and powerful that the fighting would stop immediately.

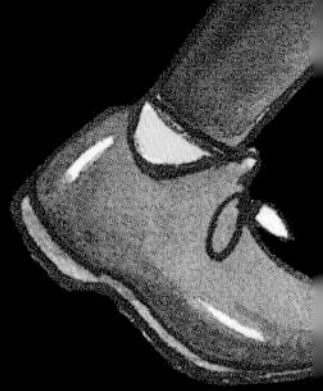

Look out!
Here comes
Gussy.

Later on, to make himself fit so that he could join the Punc Police, Fergus would go to the gym four times a week.

First he would do press-ups:

Press-up.

STOP.

Count 10.

Down.

Then he would use the dumb-bells:

Lift. STOP. Hold. Down.

With his strong arms and hands, he became the Puncs' top weight-lifter.

When he's on duty, Fergus often has to raise his arms. He can instantly bring cars, vans, lorries, motorbikes and bicycles to a halt (which is the same as a Full Stop).

Fergus's mother, Betty, is a Lollipop Lady. She stops traffic so that children can cross the road. She hates to see them behaving badly.

"I'll soon put a STOP to that,"

she says sternly.

Fergus's father, Mick, is a security officer at a factory. He stops visitors and asks them to show their passes, so that he can raise the barrier.

He even uses a STOPWATCH

to time them in and out.

Fergus has a brother, Jock, who is in the P.M.P. (Punc Mounted Police).
He and his fearless horse, STOPWELL, know how to STOP hooligans from making a nuisance of themselves.

P.C.C

Fergus is a keen sportsman. In summer, he plays cricket for the P.C.C. (Punc Cricket Club). With his strong arms and safe pair of hands, he is a very good wicket-keeper.

He crouches behind the stumps and stops balls.
This means that he also stops the batsmen from scoring runs.

In winter, Fergus plays football
for the P.U.F.C.
(Punc United Football Club).
With his strong arms and safe
pair of hands, he is a first-class
goal-keeper.

To stop the ball going into
the net he dives
and leaps.

When the spectators see who is in goal, it stops the hooligans among them from shouting rude words or throwing things onto the pitch.

Fergus tries to be friendly as well as firm. But there is one Punc who really makes him angry, and that is Colin Comma, who always seems to be in his way. Fergus likes to bring sentences to a. But Colin just goes on,

and on, and, on, and on, and on, and on, and on,
and on, and on, and on,
and on, and on,

No STOPPING here!
PUNC1

Fergus has a useful way of shortening words. When he is writing quick notes, he uses lots of Full Stops all over the place.

Fergus and his family don't think much of Full Stops who call themselves fancy names, such as Point or Full Point.

However, they are quite happy about their Canadian relations, Patsy and Pete Period, who work for the Punc Park Police. The Periods stop visitors from feeding the animals and lighting fires.

STOP that at once, or we'll take you away!

Stop and think.

As you can see, Fergus is a V.I.P.

(Very Important Punc):

1. He stops the words from wandering about.

2. He brings sentences to a .

3. He saves space by shortening words.

4. He is useful for making lists, like this one.

5. Without him, Ethel Exclamation Mark and Quentin Question Mark would have something missing.

6. Finally, he is the only Punc who can bring this, or any other, book to a .

Fergus's Checklist

- **Every sentence must start with a capital letter and end with a full stop (unless a question mark or an exclamation mark is used instead), like this:**
  Fergus is very fit.

- **Use a full stop after the initial letters of your name, like this:**
  F. F. S. (Fergus Full Stop).

- **Use a full stop in titles:**
  Mr. And Mrs. Full Stop
  Dr. Punctone

- **Use a full stop for shortening long words, like this:**
  P. U. F. C. (Punc United Football Club)
  This will make them easier to remember and quicker to write.

- **Use full stops to write dates, like this:**
  12.02.08

- **Full stops are useful for writing a memo or note, like this:**
  Check in at work. Traffic duty. Go to gym. Lunch. Mend motorbike.

- **Full stops are used to punctuate abbreviations like these:**
  e.g. (for example); i.e. (in other words); etc. (and so on)

- **Use a full stop after numbers or letters when you are writing down the points in a list, like this:**
  1. Get up
  2. Get dressed
  3. Have breakfast

- **Use full stops to record the time, like this:**
  It is 5.30 p.m.

- **Decimal sums also need full stops (called decimal points), like this one:**
  12.5 + 15.2 + 9.8 = 37.5

- **Full stops are important in codes, like this one:**
  S.O.S

- **The full stop is very fashionable. Just look at Fergus's e-mail address:**
  fergus.fullstop@puncmail.com